How to use this book

Say the sound.

Trace the letter shapes.

Point to the picture and say the word.

Blend to read the list of words.

ai ee igh

ai

aim

rain
nail
paid
train

j v w -x y z -zz qu

What other words can you find in the picture with the /ai/ sound in them?

*[w**ai**st, s**ai**ling boat]*

ch sh th -ng ai

ee

eel

bee
week
need
tree

ch sh th -ng ai ee

/ee/ can also be spelled like this: **y** **happy**

What other words can you find in the picture with the /ee/ sound in them?

*[ch**ee**k, t**ee**th, st**ee**l band, thr**ee** drums, h**ee**l, gr**ee**n dress]*

igh

knight

sigh
night
light
fright

Say the sounds

sh th -ng ai ee -igh

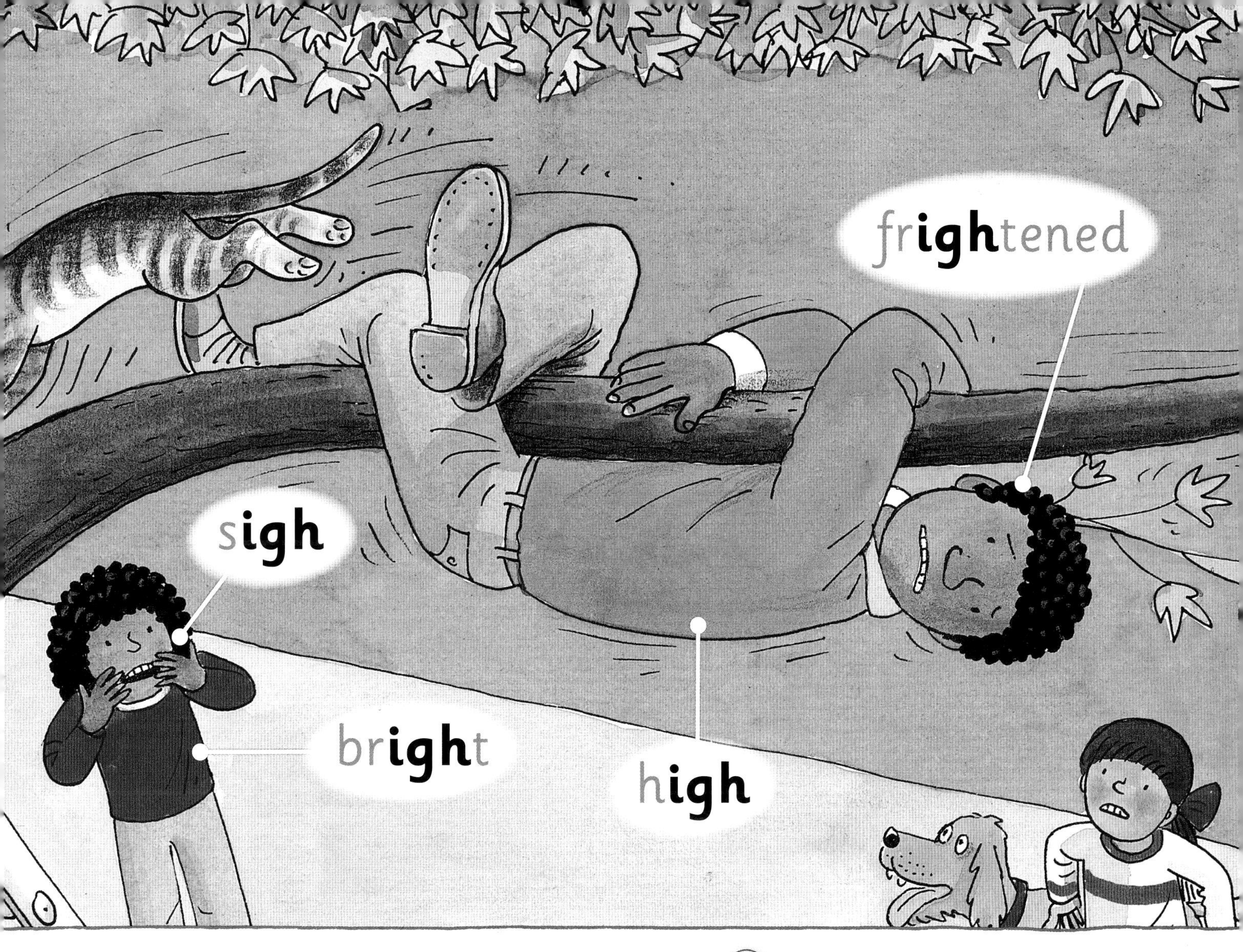

What other words can you find in the picture with the /igh/ sound in them?

*[thi**gh**, sunli**gh**t]*

/igh/ can also be spelled like this:

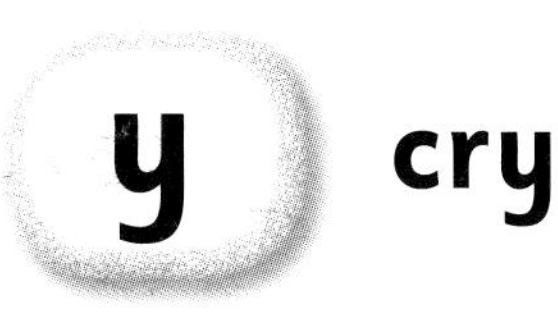

cry

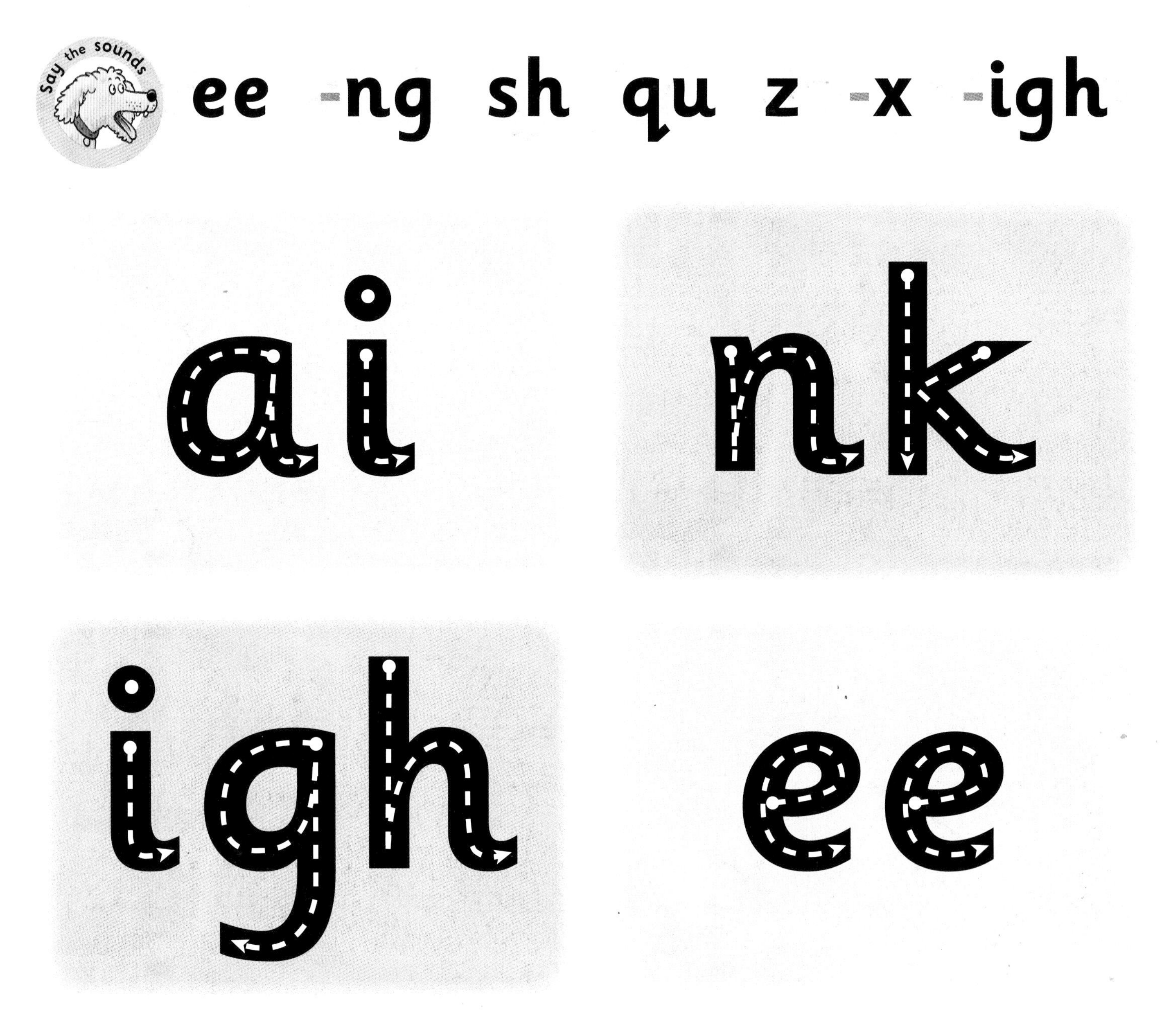

Trace the graphemes and say the sounds.

ai th ch w y j v -zz

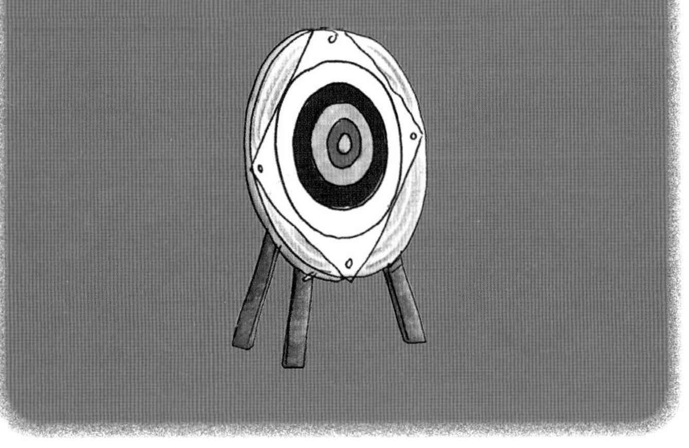

Match the pictures to the graphemes.

three big feet

No peeking!

The ship sets sail.

This seed needs light.

The snail waits for rain.

Did the knight get a fright?

Read the captions. Which captions are sentences?

-ng ch -igh th ai sh ee

Match the captions to the pictures. Which two captions do not have a picture?

"Say the sounds" ch sh th -ng ai ee -igh

Bees seek,
Snails feed,
The knight peeks,
And I sleep.

A ship sails,
The maid wails,
The night train fails,
And I sleep.

Read the poem. Sound out and blend any words that you do not know.